A David Bennett Book

For Alexander
R. T.

For Kate & Matthew
A. S.

First published in 1992 by
Kingfisher Books,
Grisewood & Dempsey Ltd,
Elsley House, 24-30 Great Titchfield Street,
London W1P 7AD

BRITISH LIBRARY CATALOGUING IN PUBLICATION DATA
Thomson, Ruth
It's hard to keep an elephant.
I. Title II. Snow, Alan
591
ISBN 0 86272 860 6

Produced and directed by
David Bennett Books Ltd,
94 Victoria Street, St Albans,
Herts, AL1 3TG

Typesetting by Type City
Production by Imago
Printed in Hong Kong

It's Hard to Keep an Elephant

and other wild animals

written by

Ruth Thomson

illustrated by

Alan Snow

Kingfisher Books

It wasn't fair.
All my friends had got pets.
I wanted one as well.

Mum and Dad said pets were nothing
but trouble, but I pestered them
and pestered them.

In the end, they agreed I could have a cat.
But I didn't want any old cat . . .

so I got a giant cat - a furry lion.

Mum and Dad were worried at first,
but it wasn't much trouble. In fact,
it snoozed for most of the day.

Mind you, it was very hungry in the evenings.

Mum and Dad weren't too pleased
when it sharpened its claws,
but I told them all cats did that.

But when the lion ruined Mum's favourite
chair, they said it would have to go.
I thought I'd get something smaller instead . . .

so I got a skunk.

I took it for a walk to show my friends, but they didn't seem too interested.

I thought a skunk was great company, until one day, I tripped over it by mistake. It covered me with its nasty smelling spray. After that, no-one would come anywhere near me.

Mum made me wash with
tomato juice. Imagine it!
That was the only thing
which would get rid of the stink.
I had to stay in the bath for hours.

Maybe keeping a skunk wasn't
such a good idea after all.

Mum and Dad said it would have to go.
I thought I'd get something cuddly instead . . .

so I got a monkey - a howler monkey.

It made itself at home in our garden
straightaway. I gave it bananas,
oranges and other fruit to eat.
I couldn't believe what a messy eater
it was, nor could Dad.

The monkey was a very useful alarm clock.
It howled at dawn each day and woke me up.
But not everyone was pleased.
Mum and Dad got very grumpy waking up at 5 o'clock
and so did the neighbours.

Everyone said it would have to go.
I thought I'd get something quieter . . .

so I got a rattlesnake.

It hardly made any noise. It lived in the washing basket and came out to play when I got home from school.

Unfortunately, rattlesnakes are poisonous.
I didn't need to worry though, because my friend,
Ned, lent me his snake keeper's outfit.

But none of my friends would
come round to play, because
they didn't have snake keepers'
outfits like mine.

The snake's favourite game
was hide and seek.
It played all over the house.
I never knew where
I would find it next.

Mum and Dad
didn't think
this game was
at all amusing.

Dad nearly
sat on it.

Mum nearly
trod on it.

They said it would have to go.
I thought I'd get a bird instead . . .

so I got some penguins.

They spent all day and night
messing about in water.
None of us could have
a bath for weeks.
I loved watching
the penguins.
They made me
laugh and laugh.

Mum and Dad
didn't laugh at all.

We had to keep a few fish for the penguins
in the kitchen, so there wasn't room for much else.

Mum and Dad said
the penguins would have to go.
I thought I'd get something
really tiny instead . . .

so I got a pair of locusts.

They were no trouble - at first. They weren't messy or smelly. They lived quite happily in the garden and found their own food.

But one day, I found several more. Every week, there were more and more of them. They ate and ate and ate.

They ate Mr Jones' lettuces and Miss Smith's cabbages. Nothing was left of Dad's prize geraniums but the stalks.

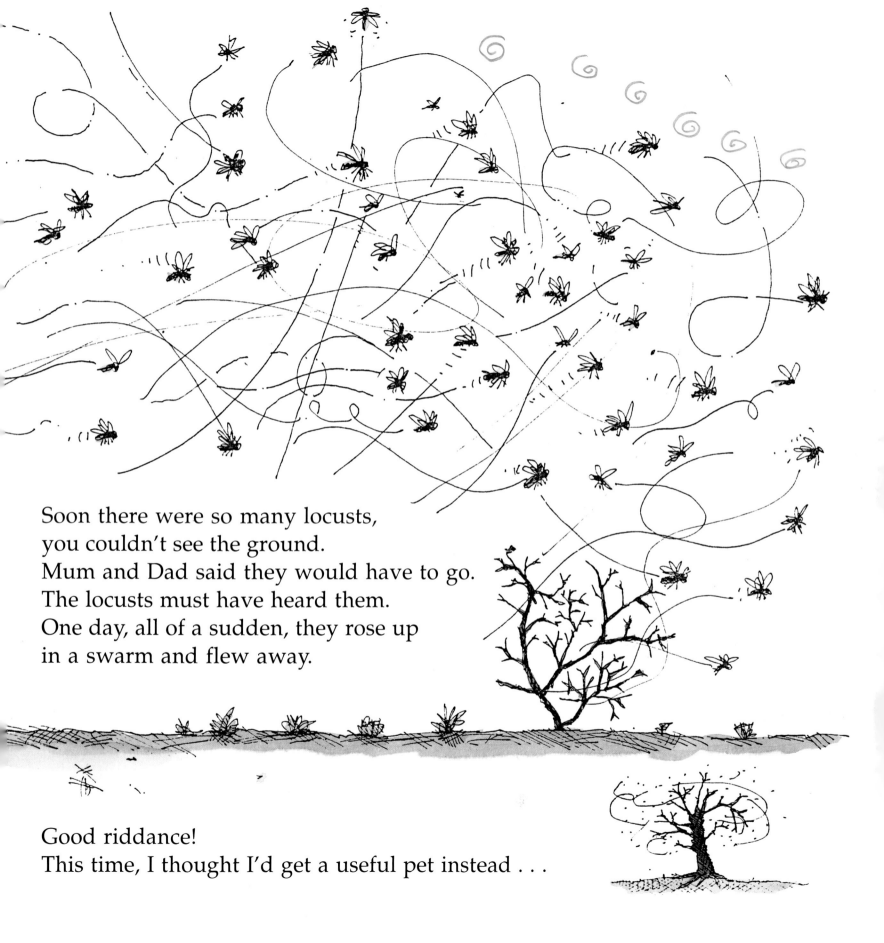

Soon there were so many locusts,
you couldn't see the ground.
Mum and Dad said they would have to go.
The locusts must have heard them.
One day, all of a sudden, they rose up
in a swarm and flew away.

Good riddance!
This time, I thought I'd get a useful pet instead . . .

so I got a camel.

Dad was pleased because he didn't have to take me
to school any more. My friends were pleased as well,
because I let them have camel rides at lunchtime.

Mind you, I wasn't so pleased when I found out
how mean a camel could be.

It spat.   It bit.   It kicked.

It also had several other nasty habits,
which I don't like to mention.

Worst of all, the camel was very, very stubborn.
One day it sat down in the hall and refused to budge.
We had to climb in and out of the windows instead.

Mum and Dad said it would have to go.
I thought I'd try another useful pet instead . . .

so I got an elephant.

I thought it would be useful for washing the car.
Mind you, it was a teeny bit bigger than I expected
and its appetite was enormous.

It pulled up most of the lawn,
broke half the shrubs and
knocked a tree over
into Mr Jones' garden.
I told Mr Jones not to worry.

I knew elephants could be trained
to lift logs. Mr Jones borrowed
mine to move the tree,
but I don't think
he trained it properly.

When the elephant had eaten
most of the garden, I had to buy it
tons and tons of hay.

I dug a big pond in the garden,
so the elephant could have a bath.
When he'd finished spraying himself,
he treated me to a shower as well.

The neighbours weren't keen on my elephant.
It kept wandering into their gardens,
probably in search of its herd. Mum and Dad said
it would have to go. I thought I'd get an animal
which could use the pond . . .

so I got a beaver.

In next to no time, it had cut down the trees,
gnawed the fence, chewed a hole
in the tool shed and munched
the struts on our veranda.

It built a lodge of branches
in the middle of the pond
and spent all day chewing twigs.

The garden was like an enormous adventure playground.

My friends and I loved it.
Mum and Dad didn't.
They were furious.

I suppose the garden was a bit of a mess.
They said the beaver would have to go.
I thought I'd get a less noticeable pet . . .

so I got some prairie dogs.

They lived in a maze of tunnels
that they dug underground,
so I didn't see much of them.

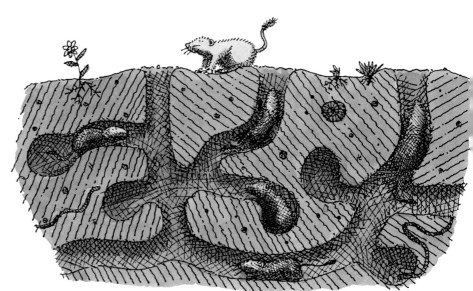

From time to time,
they came out to nibble
what was left of the grass.

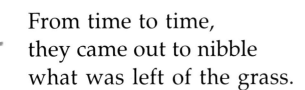

It was fun trying to guess
where they would pop out.

Mum and Dad didn't think it was fun at all.
I think they were worried about the tunnelling
under the house.

They said the prairie dogs would have to go.
They told me I couldn't have any more pets,
because they were far too much trouble.

But maybe they'll let me have a cat.
Cats are no problem.

They laze about . . .

and laze about . . .

and eat and drink . . .

and like to be
cuddled . . .

and like to be
tickled.

On the other hand,
they sleep an awful lot,
so perhaps I'll get
a crocodile instead!